NATURAL LIVING

NEAL'S YARD
COVENT GARDEN
REMEDIES

ENERGIZE

Penguin
Random
House

Editors Susannah Steel, Sarah Ruddick,
Libby Brown
Designers Alison Gardner, Kathryn Wilding,
Jacket Designer Vanessa Hamilton
Producer, Pre-Production Rebecca Fallowfield
Senior Production Controller Isobel Reid
Special Sales Creative Project Manager
Alison Donovan

Content previously published in *Neal's Yard Remedies*
(2011) by Dorling Kindersley Limited
80 Strand, London, WC2R 0RL

2 4 6 8 10 9 7 5 3 1
001 – 309662 – Dec/2017

Copyright © 2011, 2017
Dorling Kindersley Limited
A Penguin Random House Company

A CIP catalogue record for this book is available
from the British Library.

ISBN 978-0-2413-3407-2

Printed and bound in China

A WORLD OF IDEAS
SEE ALL THERE IS TO KNOW
www.dk.com

DISCLAIMER: See page 48

CONTENTS

INTRODUCTION

According to the World Health Organization, herbal remedies are the most widespread system of medicine used in the world. In many developed countries that knowledge was almost lost, but the last couple of decades have seen a renewed interest in herbal remedies, and more and more people are recognizing the many benefits of using them to treat themselves and their family.

Used appropriately, herbs can be a satisfying part of a more holistic lifestyle, and many herbs are of course the starting point of much of the modern medicine used today. When used with common sense, herbal remedies are a safe and effective form of home help. If we can treat colds, flu, or minor injuries in the early stages we can often prevent the development of something more serious and avoid using conventional drugs with their risk of side-effects.

Learning which herbs work for us enables us to learn more about the plants that surround us, as well as our own healing processes. However, some herbs are not suitable for everyone or at every stage of life (during pregnancy, for example); if in any doubt you should always consult a medical practitioner.

We have "tried and tested" all the recipes in this book, so we can promise they are delicious as well as being good for you. We are excited to have the opportunity to introduce you to some more unusual plants and flavours so you can be more adventurous whilst trusting that your health and well-being will benefit.

Neal's Yard Remedies has over thirty years of expertise and passion in creating wonderful, natural hair- and skincare products and we are delighted to share some of our favourite ways of using herbs to heal and nurture your skin. Enjoy creating and using your own herbal remedies!

Susan Curtis, Natural Health Director, Neal's Yard Remedies

Consultant's note

Hippocrates, the father of medicine, wrote: "Let food be thy medicine, and medicine be thy food". Many herbs described in this book are used both as tasty foods and as medicines, and the delicious recipes provide new ideas for combining healthy ingredients. Although the herbal medicines have not yet all been researched by modern science, most have stood the test of time. You should always see your doctor for serious health problems, but I hope this book will help readers to treat and prevent minor illnesses, and to understand treatments prescribed by their herbalist.

Dr Merlin Willcox MRCGP MCPP

Pistachio and avocado smoothie

 PROVIDES OMEGA-RICH OILS   **ENERGIZES**

Makes 2 servings

Pistachios are revered in Ayurvedic and Middle Eastern traditions as a tonic for the whole body. In traditional Chinese medicine they are believed to positively influence the liver, and especially the kidneys. The addition of avocado, hemp seed oil, and linseed oil add body and a rich blend of omega oils to this smoothie.

INGREDIENTS

50g (1¾oz) pistachios (plus a few
   for decoration)
1 small avocado, stoned, peeled,
   and quartered
1 tsp hemp seed oil
2 tsp linseed oil
juice of ½ lemon
fresh juice of 6 celery stems
freshly ground black pepper to taste
pinch of salt
3–4 fresh basil leaves
a little mineral water

METHOD

1 Put all the ingredients except the mineral water into a blender or food processor and blend until smooth. Add enough mineral water to ensure the smoothie is of a pourable consistency.
2 Serve in glasses, with a sprinkle of finely chopped pistachios on top of each.

Maca and mango smoothie

 ENERGIZES

Makes 2 servings

Maca root *(Lepidium meyenii)* does not taste tremendously interesting, but it has a reputation for invigorating the body and enhancing sexual stamina. Peruvians consider it to be a superfood. Coconut oil, linseeds, and hemp seeds all provide essential fatty acids, while fresh ripe mango provides body and flavour.

INGREDIENTS

2 large ripe mangoes
2 tsp maca root powder
2 tsp hemp seeds, shelled
2 tsp coconut oil
juice of 1 lemon
4 fresh peppermint leaves
a little mineral water (optional)

METHOD

Place all the ingredients in a blender or food processor and blend to a smooth, silky texture. Dilute with mineral water as desired, if necessary.

Plum and fennel smoothie

 DETOXES

Makes 2 servings

All the ingredients in this smoothie have a natural laxative quality. This is a good drink to take not only for occasional constipation, but also as a part of a more extensive detox regime. If you prefer a very smooth texture without bits, use a teaspoon each of linseed and hemp seed oils instead of the soaked seeds.

INGREDIENTS
9–10 large dark blue-skinned plums
½ tsp fennel seeds
2 tbsp linseeds, soaked
2 tbsp shelled hemp seeds, soaked

METHOD
1 Stew the plums first: put them in a saucepan with 250ml (9fl oz) of mineral water, add the fennel seeds, and bring to the boil. Put the lid on and simmer on a low heat for 10–12 minutes. Allow to cool.
2 Transfer to a blender or food processor, add the remaining seeds (or oils, if using) and blend to a smooth consistency.

Power berry smoothie

 NOURISHES BLOOD   **REJUVENATES, REVITALIZES**

Makes 2 servings

These fragrantly sweet but subtly tart fresh berries are a powerhouse of phytonutrients with antioxidant, antimicrobial, and anticarcinogenic properties. Their seed oil contains exceptionally high levels of vitamins E and A and omega-3 and omega-6 fatty acids, and they also protect the heart and nourish the liver.

INGREDIENTS
2 tbsp fresh raspberries
2 tbsp fresh blackberries
2 tbsp fresh blueberries
2 tbsp fresh blackcurrants
2 tsp acai berry powder
800ml (1¼ pints) lemongrass
    infusion, cold (p.29)
a little mineral water (optional)
a dash of maple syrup or a pinch
    of stevia powder (optional)

METHOD
1 Place the fresh berries and acai berry powder in a blender or food processor, add the lemongrass infusion, and blend to a smooth, silky texture.
2 If necessary, add a little mineral water to achieve a consistency you like. Ensure that most of the seeds from the fruit have been ground down so that they release their oils. Add the maple syrup or stevia powder to sweeten only if needed.

Hawthorn flower and lavender tea

 STRENGTHENS HEART, RELAXES VESSELS

 MENDS A BROKEN HEART

Makes 3–4 servings

There are some heartaches, such as overwhelming emotions, sense of loss, and lack of self-worth, that only the soft and enlightened fragrance of flowers can soothe. Hawthorn "lightens the heart", lavender relaxes the mind, rose eases a broken heart, and orange flower and jasmine encourage a desire to make things better and start anew.

INGREDIENTS

1 tsp hawthorn flowers
1 tsp lavender
1 tsp rosebuds
1 tsp orange flowers
1 tsp jasmine

METHOD

Place all the ingredients in a teapot, pour in 500ml (16fl oz) of boiling water, allow to infuse for 10–15 minutes, and serve. Drink hot or cold throughout the day.

Nettle and cleavers tea

 DETOXES

Makes 2 servings

This is a great tea for gentle cleansing at any time of the year. In spring, fresh nettles and cleavers can be juiced and drunk to cleanse and nourish the body. Cleavers helps to reduce fluid retention in the skin, reduce puffiness under the eyes, and improve the complexion. Nettles also nourish the blood and cleanse the body through increased urination.

INGREDIENTS

2 tsp nettle leaves
2 tsp cleavers

METHOD

Place the ingredients in a teapot, pour in 300ml (10fl oz) of boiling water, allow to infuse for 10–15 minutes, and serve. Drink hot or cold throughout the day.

Mullein and marshmallow tea

 RELIEVES A DRY COUGH

Makes 2 servings

Mullein leaves and flowers and marshmallow leaves, flowers, and roots all provide mucilaginous, anti-inflammatory protection for the respiratory and urinary system. This tea can also be used to treat dry coughs, nervous coughs, dry lungs, and inflamed bronchial tubes. Marshmallow leaf and plantain leaf also soothe an inflamed urinary tract.

INGREDIENTS
1 tsp mullein leaves
1 tsp marshmallow leaves
1 tsp ribwort plantain

METHOD
Place all the ingredients in a teapot, pour in 300ml (10fl oz) of boiling water, allow to infuse for 10–15 minutes, and serve. Drink hot or cold throughout the day.

Horsetail and cornsilk tea

 ACTS AS A DIURETIC   **ACTS AS A DIURETIC**

Makes 5–6 servings

This refreshing and cleansing tea is especially good for reducing occasional inflammatory conditions in the urinary system caused by non-specific micro-organisms, such as cystitis. These herbs not only increase urination, they also cool irritation and soothe inflammation of the urinary system, and contain potassium.

INGREDIENTS
2 tsp horsetail
2 tsp corn silk
2 tsp dandelion leaves
2 tsp cleavers
2 tsp ribwort plantain leaves

METHOD
Place all the ingredients in a teapot, pour in 600ml (1 pint) of boiling water, allow to infuse for 10–15 minutes, and serve. Drink hot or cold throughout the day.

Dandelion (Taraxacum officinale)
The leaves are extremely rich in vitamins and minerals, and are a good source of calcium.

Lemon balm and honey purée

 RELAXES

Makes 125g (4½oz)

This purée, which uses fresh, young, juicy lemon balm leaves, is best prepared in late spring before the plant becomes somewhat woody and the leaves less juicy. It works well as a sweetener for other herbal infusions or summer cocktails, and can be served as a hot or cold drink by adding one or two teaspoons of the purée to boiling or chilled water.

INGREDIENTS
20g (¾oz) fresh lemon balm leaves
100g (3½oz) runny honey
Juice of ½ lemon

METHOD
1 Place the leaves in a blender or food processor, add the honey and lemon juice, and blend until you get a smooth green purée.
2 Dilute with water and drink. The purée will last for a week or two, if kept refrigerated.

Sour cherry syrup

 QUICKENS MUSCLE RECOVERY   **REGULATES SLEEP**

Makes approx 600ml (1 pint)

Long-distance runners take cherry juice concentrates before and after exercising, as the anti-inflammatory properties of cherries aid quicker muscle recovery and pain release. Sour cherries also help to preserve a youthful appearance, benefit liver function, and regulate sleep patterns. Approximately 200 cherries (660g/1lb 5oz) produce 400ml (14fl oz) of cherry juice.

INGREDIENTS
400ml (14fl oz) sour cherry juice, freshly pressed
250g (9oz) sugar

METHOD
1 Pour the juice into a saucepan, add the sugar, and heat gently. Dissolve the sugar in the juice, stirring constantly, then simmer for 20 minutes on a low heat.
2 Strain the syrup and bottle in a sterilized glass bottle with a tight-fitting lid. Keep refrigerated and use within a few weeks.
3 Drink diluted with cold or hot mineral water.

Lemon balm (*Melissa officinalis*)
has cooling, sedative, and uplifting properties; it lowers fever and improves digestion.

HOW TO MAKE TINCTURES

Tinctures are concentrated, alcohol-based extracts of plant materials, and are much more portable and long-lasting than herbal teas. These recipes enable you to produce simple extracts and further explore the benefits of medicinal herbs.

Peppermint and thyme tincture

 CALMS A NERVOUS GUT

INGREDIENTS
25g (scant 1oz) peppermint
15g (½oz) thyme
25g (scant 1oz) chamomile
20g (¾oz) yarrow
15g (½oz) liquorice root
500ml (16fl oz) good-quality vodka

Makes approx 500ml (16fl oz)

This tincture tastes good enough to serve as an aperitif. It aids digestion and benefits the activity of the large intestine, and helps to expel wind and soothe a nervous stomach. Use within 6 months.

NOTE: This tincture is not suitable for use during pregnancy.

1 *Place all the ingredients* except the vodka in a large jar.

2 *Cover with the vodka,* stir, and make sure all the ingredients are well immersed. Seal the jar tightly and place it in a dark cupboard. Give the jar a few good shakes every day for 3 weeks.

3 *Open the jar* and strain the ingredients through a muslin-lined sieve into a shallow bowl. Discard the ingredients in the muslin and pour the liquid into an amber glass bottle. Label the tincture bottle with the names of all the ingredients and the date. Take 1 teaspoon in a glass of warm or cold water and sip before or after meals.

Goji berry and Siberian ginseng tincture

 ENERGIZES

Makes 300–350ml (10–12fl oz)

This tincture enhances the body's natural defences and improves mental concentration, physical endurance, and a sense of well-being. It does this by energizing the body, especially the liver and the nervous, hormonal, and immune systems. If you can't find fresh oat tops (the top 20cm (8in) of the plant), use the dried oats available from grocers and supermarkets.

INGREDIENTS

25g (scant 1oz) goji berries
25g (scant 1oz) Siberian ginseng
  (*Eleutherococcus senticosus*)
25g (scant 1oz) oat tops or dried oats
20g (¾oz) schisandra berries
5g (⅛oz) liquorice root
400ml (14fl oz) good-quality vodka

METHOD

1 Ensure that all the dried ingredients are finely chopped, but not powdered.
2 Place all the ingredients except the vodka into a large glass jar with a secure-fitting lid. Pour in the vodka, close the lid tightly, and shake a few times.
3 Label the jar with all the ingredients and the date. Place the jar in a dark cupboard and shake it at least once every day for 3 weeks.
4 Strain the contents of the jar through a muslin bag into a measuring jug and pour the tincture into an appropriately sized (350–400ml/12–14fl oz) sterilized amber glass bottle. Seal the bottle.
5 Label with all the ingredients and the original starting date. Start by taking a few drops each day and build up to 1 teaspoon 2–3 times a day. Use within 6 months.

NOTE: This tincture is not suitable for use during pregnancy.

Red clover and cleavers tincture

 **SOOTHES INFLAMED SKIN**

Makes 300–350ml (10–12fl oz)

These herbs are all used for acute and chronic skin inflammation, including acne, eczema, psoriasis, and other skin conditions. They help to detoxify the body and eliminate waste via the urine, and have a laxative effect. They also stimulate the gall bladder and liver. It is worth noting that serious skin conditions always require professional advice.

INGREDIENTS

15g (½oz) red clover
15g (½oz) cleavers
20g (¾oz) viola (heartsease)
20g (¾oz) violet leaves (*Viola odorata*)
20g (¾oz) mahonia root (*Mahonia aquifolium*), finely chopped
20g (¾oz) gotu kola
400ml (14fl oz) good-quality vodka

METHOD

1 Ensure that all the dried ingredients are finely chopped, but not powdered.
2 Place all the ingredients except the vodka into a large glass jar with a secure-fitting lid. Pour in the vodka, close the lid tightly, and shake a few times.
3 Label the jar with all the ingredients and the date. Place the jar in a dark cupboard and shake it at least once every day for 3 weeks.
4 Strain the contents of the jar through a muslin bag into a measuring jug and pour the tincture into an appropriately sized (350–400ml/12–14fl oz) sterilized amber glass bottle. Seal the bottle.
5 Label with all the ingredients and the original starting date. Start by taking a few drops each day and build up to 1 teaspoon 2–3 times a day. Use within 6 months.

NOTE: This tincture is not suitable for use during pregnancy.

Nettle and sweet potato soup

 **PURIFIES SKIN**    **ACTS AS A SPRINGTIME TONIC**

Makes 4 servings

Nettle soup is a classic spring cleanser that has been used as a health tonic for generations in Europe; nettles are full of vitamins and minerals and purify the blood, clear toxins, lower blood pressure, and improve the quality of skin and hair.

INGREDIENTS

1 tbsp olive oil
1 medium-sized onion, or
    4 shallots, chopped
1 medium-sized sweet potato,
    chopped into small pieces
2 garlic cloves, squeezed
1 litre (1¾ pints) vegetable stock
250g (9oz) young nettle leaves,
    washed and chopped
salt and freshly ground black pepper
2–3 tbsp barley miso paste
4 tsp half-fat crème fraîche, or
    plain yoghurt

METHOD

1 Heat the oil in a saucepan and sauté the onions or shallots and sweet potato for 2–3 minutes. Add the garlic and stock and bring to the boil. Simmer for 20 minutes, then add the nettles and turn off the heat.
2 Pour the soup into a blender or food processor and blend until smooth.
3 Season to taste with salt and pepper and the miso paste. Serve in individual bowls, each with a swirl (1 teaspoon) of crème fraiche or yoghurt.

Goji berry and mint soup

 REJUVENATES SKIN

Makes 4 servings

Goji berries are a rich source of antioxidants and a tonic that alleviates anxiety and stress, promotes a lighter, more cheerful mood, improves sleep, and increases energy and strength.

INGREDIENTS

100g (3½oz) dried goji berries
1 tbsp olive oil
3 shallots, peeled and finely chopped
2 beef tomatoes, skinned and
    finely chopped
600ml (1 pint) vegetable stock
1 tbsp fresh mint leaves, chopped,
    plus extra to garnish

METHOD

1 Wash the berries and soak them in water for a few minutes to rehydrate them. Heat the oil in a saucepan, sauté the shallots for a few minutes, then add the tomatoes and goji berries. Stir for few minutes before adding the stock. Stir and simmer for a further 20 minutes.
2 Add the mint leaves and remove from the heat. Pour the mixture into a blender or food processor and pulse until smooth. Serve garnished with the extra mint leaves.

NOTE: To skin the tomatoes, cut a cross incision through the skin at the base of the tomato and place in a heatproof bowl. Pour over boiling water to cover and leave to stand for a few minutes. Remove the tomatoes from the water with a slotted spoon. The skin should now peel away easily.

Ginseng and astragalus longevity soup

 ENERGIZING　　 **ENHANCES DIGESTION**

Makes 4 servings

The energizing ingredients in this soup include ginseng, which enhances energy levels and restores strength after a prolonged illness, and astragalus root, which is well known for its beneficial effect on the immune system. It strengthens the lungs, helps to prevent colds, and alleviates any shortness of breath. Chinese black fungus is rich in amino acids, phosphorus, iron, and calcium.

INGREDIENTS

15g (½oz) Chinese black fungus
(hei mu er/*Auricularia auricula*)
15g (½oz) fresh or dried
  astragalus root
15g (½oz) fresh or dried ginseng root
6 shallots, topped and tailed with
  the skins left on
3 garlic cloves, topped and tailed with
  the skins left on
1 large carrot, scrubbed
2.5cm (1in) cube fresh ginger root,
  thinly sliced
150g (5½oz) fresh shiitake
  mushrooms
150g (5½oz) fresh oyster mushrooms
1 large piece wakame seaweed, cut
  into small pieces, or 1 tbsp dried
15g (½oz) goji berries, pre-soaked
  if dried
200g (7oz) buckwheat or
  soba, noodles
2–3 tbsp barley miso paste
1 handful of flat-leaf parsley, chopped
freshly ground black pepper

METHOD

1 Put the fungus, astragalus root, ginseng root, shallots, garlic, whole carrot, and ginger into a large saucepan, cover with 1.5 litres (2¾ pints) of water and bring to the boil. Simmer on a very low heat for half an hour with the lid on tightly.

2 Take the pan off the heat, strain the liquid through a colander or sieve, and return it to the pan. Discard the astragalus root and ginseng. Squeeze the garlic and shallots from their skins and return them to the soup. Slice the fungus and carrot into small pieces and return them to the soup. Add the mushrooms and wakame seaweed and bring the soup back to simmering point. Add the goji berries. After 10 minutes, add the buckwheat noodles and let them cook through for 5–7 minutes.

3 Serve in individual bowls. Allow each person to add enough barley miso paste to their liking and garnish with the parsley and a grinding of black pepper.

Roasted barley and chestnut soup

 STRENGTHEN LOWER LIMBS   **ENERGIZES**

Makes 4 servings

This tonic soup makes a great nourishing lunch on a cold winter's day, as it primarily supports kidney energy. It will help to warm up the whole system, and eating it once a week during the winter season is most useful for individuals suffering from aches and pains aggravated by the cold weather.

INGREDIENTS

6 shallots, topped and tailed,
  with skin left on
4 cloves garlic with skin left on
2 large carrots, washed
200g (7oz) celeriac, peeled and cubed
2½cm (1in) fresh ginger root, washed
150g (5½oz) sweet chestnuts, fresh
  or precooked
200g (7oz) shiitake mushrooms,
  stalks removed and sliced
2 long blades wakame seaweed,
  chopped into small pieces, or
  2 tbsp wakame flakes
100g (3½oz) roasted barley
  (see note below)
1 tbsp barley miso
flat-leaf parsley, to garnish (optional)

METHOD

1 If using fresh chestnuts, roast them first (see note below).
2 Put the whole shallots, garlic, carrots, celeriac, and ginger into a large saucepan, cover with 500ml (16fl oz) of water, and bring to a simmer. Cook, covered, over a low heat for at least 1 hour, occasionally adding some more water if necessary.
3 Take the saucepan off the heat and strain the liquid through a colander into a clean saucepan. Pick out the garlic and shallots from the cooked vegetables and squeeze them out of their skins directly into the liquid.
4 Add the chestnuts to the soup and bring to the boil. Add the mushrooms, wakame seaweed, and roasted barley, and simmer for 15–20 minutes. Then stir in the barley miso until dissolved, remove from the heat, and serve in bowls with the parsley garnish (if using).

NOTE: To roast barley, soak it overnight in lukewarm water, drain, and leave to dry on a tray covered with a clean cloth. When the barley is still damp, heat a large frying pan over a high heat. Turn the heat down to medium, and add a quarter of the barley, stirring constantly. When the grain is golden brown and makes a gravelly noise as you stir it, tip it out of the pan and allow to cool completely on a plate. Repeat with the remaining 3 batches. Store in an airtight jar if you prepare the barley a few days before making the soup.

NOTE: To roast fresh chestnuts, chip into the apex, or tip, of each nut with a sharp knife and place them on a baking tray. Bake in the oven at 180°C (350°F/Gas 4) for 20–25 minutes. Take them out of the oven. Wrap each chestnut in a cloth and squeeze hard to crush the shell, then peel it all off.

MAKING FRUIT BARS

These recipes will help you to incorporate more wild fruits, nuts, and grains into your diet. The variations on these basic ingredients are endless, and depend mainly on the way the grains are prepared, as well as your choice of dried fruits, nuts, and seeds.

Four fruits power bar

 NOURISHES BLOOD

INGREDIENTS

150g (5½oz) wheat grains
150g (5½oz) dry apricots
50g (1¾oz) raisins
50g (1¾oz) blackcurrants
50g (1¾oz) sour cherries
50g (1¾oz) walnuts, soaked for 4 hours, dried, and lightly pan-toasted
50g (1¾oz) sesame seeds, pan-toasted

Makes 16 bars

Sour cherries bring a sharp, lively flavor to these power bars. Add a combination of other dried berries, fruits, or nuts if you like, to complement the flavour of the sour cherries. These bars are best eaten the day you make them, not only to keep them from spoiling, but to get the maximum goodness from the freshly sprouted grains.

1 To sprout the wheat grains, soak for 12 hours or overnight. Rinse the grains thoroughly and put in a large glass jar (grains expand to two to three times their initial volume). Cover the opening and neck of the jar with muslin cloth and attach it with string or a strong rubber band. Place at a 45° angle in a well-lit spot but not in direct sunlight. Rinse the grains each morning and evening by pouring water through the muslin and emptying it out.

2 The sprouts are ready when seedlings approximately 0.5–1cm (¼in) in length appear. Rinse the seedlings thoroughly in clean water, strain, and spread on a clean cloth to dry. The sprouted grains are ready to use when they are dry to the touch. Place the apricots and raisins in a blender and blend to a paste. Add half of the sprouted grains and blackcurrants and blend until crushed (but not blended to a purée).

3 Transfer to a mixing bowl and add the rest of the grains, berries, and the cherries. Mix well with a wooden spoon. Chop the walnuts into small chunks and add them to the mix. Sprinkle the sesame seeds on a flat surface. Roll out the mixture, or press it with clean hands, over the seeds into a rectangle 1cm (½in) thick. Use a sharp knife to cut the mixture into small rectangular bars. Place the bars on a rack and leave to dry out for a few hours.

Cranberry and apricot power bars

 ENERGIZES

Makes 12–16 bars

Barley has long had a reputation as a highly nutritious cereal; it was eaten by Ancient Greek athletes and Roman gladiators, who were known as *hordearii* ("barley eaters"). Cranberries are packed with antioxidants, and apricots are an excellent source of iron, so these power bars make a highly nutritious and sustaining snack to keep your energy levels up.

INGREDIENTS

150g (5½oz) lightly toasted barley, ground to a powder
100g (3½oz) dried cranberries (presoaked and dried on a cloth or tea towel)
200g (7oz) dried apricots (washed and dried on a cloth or tea towel)
60g (2oz) pistachios, coarsely chopped
40g (1¼oz) pistachios, finely ground

METHOD

1 Prepare the barley first (see below). Put the fruit and coarsely chopped pistachios in a blender or food processor and blend into a thick purée. Then add just enough of the toasted barley powder to make a pliable dough.

2 Sprinkle half the finely ground pistachios onto a flat surface, place the fruit dough on top, and roll it out into a rectangular shape about 6–8mm (¼–½in) thick. Sprinkle the top of the dough with the remaining finely ground pistachios and press them by hand into the mixture.

3 Cut into 3 x10cm (1¼ x 4in) rectangles and place on a baking tray. Bake in a preheated oven at 50°C (122°F/Gas¼) for 2–3 hours until the bars have dried out.

4 Carefully lift the bars off the tray, allow to cool on a wire rack, then wrap them individually in cling film or greaseproof paper. If wrapped and stored in a tin in a cool place, the bars can last for more than a week.

NOTE: To roast barley, soak it overnight in lukewarm water, drain, and leave to dry on a tray covered with a clean cloth. When the barley is still damp, heat a large frying pan over a high heat. Turn the heat down to medium, and add a quarter of the barley, stirring constantly. When the grain is golden brown and makes a gravelly noise as you stir it, tip it out of the pan and allow to cool completely on a plate. Repeat with the remaining 3 batches. Allow the grain to cool completely and store in an airtight container. Grind the toasted grains in a pestle and mortar to make a barley powder.

Linseed and chilli crackers

 PROVIDES OMEGA-3 FATTY ACIDS

Makes approx 12

These healthy crackers can be enjoyed by everyone. Linseed is a valuable food in a balanced diet owing to its high levels of omega-3 fatty acids, which play an essential role in strengthening immunity and maintaining good blood vessel health. The addition of seaweeds, chilli, and fresh parsley make these crackers taste very moreish.

INGREDIENTS

250g (9oz) linseeds
juice of 5 medium-sized carrots
   and 2 celery stems
1 small or medium chilli (according
   to taste), chopped
4 tbsp fresh parsley, finely chopped
4 tbsp dulse or wakame flakes
a large pinch of salt
a sprinkle of chilli powder (optional)

METHOD

1 Add the linseeds to the freshly made carrot and celery juice, then stir in the chilli, parsley, seaweed flakes, salt to taste, and chilli powder (if using). Leave for up to 2 hours to allow the linseeds to soak up the juices.
2 Spread the soaked linseeds in a thin layer on a piece of baking parchment on a baking tray. Bake in a very low oven (50°C/122°F/Gas¼) for 3–4 hours.
3 Use a knife to cut the crackers into squares. Thicker pieces can be served instead of bread with soup.

Mint and cucumber side salad with cashew nut cream

 COOLS THE DIGESTIVE SYSTEM

Makes 4 servings

You can happily share this fresh-tasting, minty raita with friends who do not eat milk or milk-related products. Cucumbers are cooling, so this dish is ideal for summer dining; if you serve it in winter, add some finely chopped fresh chilli. Use young cucumbers, which have small, compact seeds, or scoop out the larger seeds from a mature cucumber with a spoon.

INGREDIENTS

1 medium cucumber, peeled
a few fresh mint leaves, finely
   chopped, to garnish
FOR THE CASHEW NUT CREAM
75g (2½ oz) raw cashew nuts, pre-soaked
2 garlic cloves, crushed
2 tsp white miso
2 tbsp freshly squeezed lemon juice
1 tbsp fresh mint leaves, finely chopped
1 tbsp fresh coriander leaves,
   finely chopped

METHOD

1 Cut the cucumber in half lengthways and scoop out any large seeds with a spoon. Dice the cucumber finely and place in a serving bowl.
2 Put all the ingredients for the cashew nut cream in a blender or food processor, and blend thoroughly. Add 150ml (5fl oz) of water or more to adjust the consistency to that of a pouring cream.
3 Pour the cashew nut cream over the cucumber and stir together well. Sprinkle with finely chopped mint leaves.

Blackcurrant and walnut bars

 ENERGIZES

Makes 8 or more bars

If barley grain is soaked in warm water, it cooks very slowly, allowing for little loss of nutrients. Toasted grain is very crunchy and can be partially cracked or milled by laying it in a thin layer on a wooden chopping board and rolling over it with a rolling pin, before using to roll out the bars. Eat the bars within 1–2 days while still fresh.

INGREDIENTS

250g (9oz) barley grains
50g (1¾oz) walnut pieces
100g (3½oz) pitted dates
100g (3½oz) dried blackcurrants
   (or blueberries)

METHOD

1 Wash the barley grains, then soak them in warm water overnight. In the morning, drain the grains, and allow them to dry out for few minutes in a colander. Set aside 150g (5½oz) of the grain and spread the rest in a thin layer over a clean, dry cloth to dry until the next day.

2 The 150g (5½oz) of grain you set aside should still be damp, but no longer wet, and will be ready to toast. Heat a large frying pan over a high heat, then turn the heat down and add the barley in small batches to toast. Make sure that the pan is not too crowded, and that the size of the pan allows for an equal toasting of all the barley grains. Stir constantly until the grain is a golden tan colour and makes a gravelly sound as you stir it.

3 Allow the grain to cool completely, then move it in batches into a pestle and mortar and grind until lightly milled.

4 Toast the walnuts in the same way as the barley, toasting it lightly until golden with a nutty scent.

5 Once the barley grain and walnuts are ready to use, place the untoasted batch of barley grains in a blender or food processor with the dates and whizz to a paste. Turn out into a mixing bowl and stir in the blackcurrants and walnuts. Spread the toasted barley grains over a work surface and place the paste mixture on top, rolling it out into a rectangle or pressing it into shape with clean hands. Cut into bars and place on a rack to dry out.

Geranium and orange body butter

 MOISTURIZES SKIN   **HARMONIZES EMOTIONS**

Makes 100g (3½oz)

A rich and deeply nourishing body butter like this is ideal for dry skin. The essential fatty acid combination of grapeseed and almond oils act to enrich and nourish the skin by strengthening and improving its suppleness. Geranium and orange essential oils also help to tone the skin, and impart a bright, sunny scent.

INGREDIENTS

1 tbsp beeswax
3 tbsp calendula macerated oil
4 tsp grapeseed oil
4 tsp almond oil
20 drops geranium essential oil
20 drops orange essential oil

METHOD

1 Heat the beeswax, calendula, grapeseed and almond oils in a bowl set over a saucepan of boiling water (bain-marie). As the mixture cools, stir in the essential oils.
2 Pour into a sterilized dark glass jar with a tight-fitting lid, and leave to set. Use within 3 months.

Rose body butter

 MOISTURIZES SKIN   **REVITALIZES**

Makes 100g (3½oz)

If you want a luxurious and gorgeously scented body butter for nurturing the skin, this is the best choice. This aromatic balm features a triple dose of roses – macerated petal oil, rose absolute, and wild rose hip seed oil – to create a nurturing blend that softens, smoothes, and scents the skin. Geranium and patchouli give depth to the fragrance, making it truly special.

INGREDIENTS

1 tbsp beeswax
3 tbsp rose macerated oil
2 tbsp almond oil
2 tsp rosehip oil
10 drops rose absolute essential oil
10 drops geranium essential oil
5 drops patchouli essential oil

METHOD

1 Heat the beeswax, rose, almond, and rosehip oils in a bowl set over a saucepan of boiling water (bain-marie). As the mixture cools, stir in the essential oils.
2 Pour into a sterilized dark glass jar with a tight-fitting lid, and leave to set. Use within 3 months.

Lavender body balm

 MOISTURIZES SKIN   **RELAXES**

Makes 100g (3½oz)

In this creamy and rich body balm with a deeply relaxing fragrance, skin-softening coconut oil is blended with gently moisturizing and soothing almond oil to nourish and nurture the skin. Lavender, and its richly scented cousin, lavandin, are both healing and soothing on the skin and are combined here to give a relaxing fragrance.

INGREDIENTS
55g (2oz) coconut oil
2 tbsp almond oil
1 tbsp beeswax
30 drops lavender essential oil
10 drops lavandin essential oil

METHOD
1 Heat the coconut and almond oils with the beeswax in a bowl set over a saucepan of boiling water (bain-marie). As the mixture cools, stir in the essential oils.
2 Pour into a sterilized dark glass jar with a tight-fitting lid, and leave to set. Use within 3 months.

Soothing herbal balm

 TREATS BRUISES, GRAZES, AND STINGS

Makes 40g (1½oz)

An all-purpose emergency salve for bumps, bruises, bites, and grazes, this is an essential first aid remedy to keep at home. The therapeutic blend of herbal extracts, including St John's wort, calendula, and gotu kola, are combined with antiseptic myrrh and niaouli oils to help ease all manner of skin irritations and soothe grazes.

INGREDIENTS
4½ tsp calendula
   macerated oil
2 tsp St John's wort (hypericum)
   macerated oil
8g (1½ tsp) beeswax
12 drops myrrh essential oil
12 drops lavender essential oil
4 drops niaouli essential oil
4 drops echinacea tincture
4 drops gotu kola tincture

METHOD
1 Heat the calandula oil and St John's wort oil with the beeswax in a bowl set over a saucepan of boiling water (bain-marie). As the mixture cools, stir in the essential oils and tinctures.
2 Pour into a sterilized dark glass jar with a tight-fitting lid, and leave to set. Use within 3 months.

Balancing lemon moisturizer

 MOISTURIZES OILY AND PROBLEM SKIN

Makes 40g (1½oz)

Mineral-rich, anti-inflammatory nettle and cleansing lavender infusions make this light cream an ideal moisturizer for oily or problem skin. The addition of lemon essential oil, which is machine-pressed from the peel of the ripe, fresh fruit and then distilled, has a toning, tightening effect on the pores and helps to regulate the oiliness of the skin.

INGREDIENTS

1 tsp beeswax
1 tsp cocoa butter
3 tbsp grapeseed oil
2 tsp emulsifying wax
2 tbsp lavender and nettle (50:50 mix) infusion (p.29)
10 drops lemon essential oil

METHOD

1 Heat the beeswax, cocoa butter, and grapeseed oil in a bowl set over a saucepan of boiling water (bain-marie).
2 Dissolve the emulsifying wax in the freshly made, and still warm, lavender and nettle infusion.
3 Slowly add the infusion to the oil mixture, using a fast whisking action for about 10 seconds. When the mixture has cooled, stir in the lemon essential oil.
4 Store in a sterilized dark glass jar with a tight-fitting lid in the refrigerator, and use within 2 months.

Marshmallow moisturizer

 MOISTURIZES DRY SKIN

Makes 40g (1½oz)

A deeply enriching, nourishing moisturizer suitable for dry skin, this rich blend of cocoa butter and avocado and almond oils ensures that skin will remain supple and well protected from any moisture loss. Marshmallow has a soothing, softening effect, and geranium and bergamot essential oils are toning and refreshing.

INGREDIENTS

1 tsp beeswax
1 tsp cocoa butter
1 tbsp avocado oil
2 tbsp almond oil
2 tsp emulsifying wax
2 tbsp marshmallow infusion (p.29)
4 drops geranium essential oil
5 drops bergamot essential oil

METHOD

1 Heat the beeswax, cocoa butter, avocado, and almond oils in a bowl set over a saucepan of boiling water (bain-marie).
2 Dissolve the emulsifying wax in the freshly made, and still warm, infusion.
3 Slowly add the infusion to the oil mixture, using a fast whisking action for about 10 seconds. When the mixture has cooled, stir in the essential oils.
4 Store in a sterilized dark glass jar with a tight-fitting lid in the refrigerator, and use within 2 months.

Rose and geranium moisturizer

 MOISTURIZES SKIN

Makes 40g (1½oz)

This is a light moisturizer for normal skin, with a fresh, floral scent. Apricot is a wonderful skin-conditioning oil, and here it is combined with light, easily absorbed grapeseed oil and nourishing cocoa butter to enrich and smooth. Soothing rose and balancing geranium are also included to regulate moisture levels for soft, dewy skin.

INGREDIENTS

1 tsp beeswax
1 tsp cocoa butter
1 tbsp apricot kernel oil
2 tbsp grapeseed oil
2 tsp emulsifying wax
2 tbsp rose petal infusion
10 drops geranium essential oil

METHOD

1 Heat the beeswax, cocoa butter, apricot, and grapeseed oils in a bowl set over a saucepan of boiling water (bain-marie).
2 Dissolve the emulsifying wax in the freshly made, and still warm, infusion.
3 Slowly add the infusion to the oil mixture, using a fast whisking action for about 10 seconds. When the mixture has cooled, stir in the geranium essential oil.
4 Store in a sterilized dark glass jar with a tight-fitting lid in the refrigerator, and use within 2 months.

Chamomile and evening primrose moisturizer

 SOOTHES ECZEMA

Makes 100ml (3½fl oz)

A soothing, unscented cream to nurture delicate skin. Starflower and evening primrose seed oils are nature's best sources of gamma-linolenic acid (GLA) and are renowned for helping to soothe dry, itchy, or inflamed skin. Almond and cocoa butter gently moisturize, and chamomile soothes.

INGREDIENTS

1 tsp beeswax
1 tsp cocoa butter
2 tbsp almond oil
1 tsp borage seed oil
2 tsp evening primrose oil
2 tsp emulsifying wax
2 tbsp chamomile infusion (p.29)

METHOD

1 Heat the beeswax and cocoa butter with the almond, borage, and evening primrose oils in a bowl set over a saucepan of boiling water (bain-marie).
2 Dissolve the emulsifying wax in the freshly made, and still warm, chamomile infusion.
3 Slowly add the infusion to the oil mixture, using a fast whisking action for about 10 seconds. Allow to cool.
4 Store in a sterilized dark glass jar with a tight-fitting lid in the refrigerator, and use within 2 months.

Cleansing chamomile hand scrub

 EXFOLIATES

Makes 1 x 40g (1½oz) jar

Use this gentle hand cleanser as an alternative to soap. With its gently exfoliating action, enriching oats to soften and smooth, and glycerin to reduce moisture loss from the skin it both cleans and cares for hard-working hands. Chamomile flower water, which is naturally nurturing, has also been included to bring extra relief and soothe the skin.

INGREDIENTS

2 tbsp vegetable glycerin
15g (½oz) cornflour
1 tsp chamomile flower water
 (or infusion)
2 tsp ground rice
2 tsp finely ground oats

METHOD

1 Warm the vegetable glycerin in a bowl set over a saucepan of hot or boiling water (bain marie).
2 Slowly add the cornflour, stirring constantly to make a paste.
3 Take off the heat and gradually add the chamomile water, still stirring. Mix in the ground rice and oats.
4 Store in a sterilized glass jar with a tight-fitting lid and use in the same way as liquid soap. Use within 2 months.

Rose hand cream

 MOISTURIZES SKIN

Makes 85g (3oz)

Fragrant, smoothing, and nourishing, this hand cream is a perfect treat for hard-working hands. It combines restorative cold-pressed seed oil from wild roses (*Rosa canina*) with soothing flower extracts from damask roses (*Rosa* x *damascena*) to revive dry, irritated, or weather-worn skin. It also includes almond oil and cocoa butter for added moisturization.

INGREDIENTS

1½ tsp cocoa butter
1 tsp beeswax
1 tbsp almond oil
1 tbsp rosehip oil
3 tbsp rosewater
2 tsp emulsifying wax
10 drops rose absolute essential oil

METHOD

1 Melt the cocoa butter, beeswax, and almond oil in a bowl set over a saucepan of boiling water (bain marie).
2 Warm the rosewater gently in a saucepan and dissolve the emulsifying wax into it.
3 Stir the rosewater and emulsifying wax into the oily mixture very slowly and continue stirring until the cream cools.
4 Add the rose absolute essential oil and stir.
5 Store in a sterilized glass jar with a tight-fitting lid in the refrigerator, and use within 2 months.

Mandarin and myrrh foot scrub

 EXFOLIATES

Makes 1 x 40g (1½oz) jar

Foot scrubs effectively smooth away hard skin and cleanse and nourish feet to leave them feeling soft and fresh. In this scrub pumice powder effectively removes rough skin and boosts circulation, while a blend of skin-softening marshmallow herb, deeply moisturising cocoa butter, enriching apricot kernel oil, and cleansing mandarin and myrrh essential oils nourish the skin.

INGREDIENTS

15g (½oz) crushed pumice stone
10g (¼oz) cocoa butter
10g (¼oz) beeswax
3 tbsp apricot kernel oil
10g (¼oz) emulsifying wax
2 tbsp marshmallow
 infusion (see below)
12 drops myrrh essential oil
8 drops mandarin essential oil

METHOD

1 Grind the pumice stone in a pestle and mortar to a fine powder.
2 Warm the cocoa butter, beeswax, and apricot kernel oil together in a bowl set over a saucepan of boiling water (bain-marie) until all the ingredients have melted. Then remove from the heat.
3 Dissolve the emulsifying wax in the freshly made, and still warm, marshmallow infusion. Slowly add the infusion to the oily mixture and stir until cool.
4 Add the pumice stone and essential oils and mix thoroughly.
5 Store in a sterilized dark glass jar with a tight-fitting lid in the refrigerator, and use within 3 months.

Infusions

An infusion is the best way to harness the properties of the softer, green, or flowering parts of a plant. A standard therapeutic infusion is 1 heaped tsp of a single dried herb or 2 tsp of a mixture of dried herbs (for fresh herbs use double the amount) to 175ml (6fl oz) boiling water.

INGREDIENTS

1 heaped tsp dried herb, or 2 tsp
 chopped fresh herb
175ml (6fl oz) boiling water

METHOD

1 Place the chopped herbs in a cup or teapot, and pour the boiling water over the herbs.
2 Leave to steep for 10 minutes, preferably covered to avoid the loss of volatile oils in the steam. Strain the infusion before use.

Marshmallow (Althaea officinalis)
The leaves of the marshmallow plant are typically used dried for infusions, ointments, and liquid extracts.

MAKING BALMS

Balms are a simple way to nourish skin and protect it from moisture loss. Make sure that the containers you use to store your home-made balms are sterilized. If you have very sensitive skin, test any skincare product on a small area of skin first to check that it does not provoke a reaction.

Calendula and mandarin lip balm

 MOISTURIZES SKIN

 HELPS PREVENT COLD SORES

INGREDIENTS

1 tsp beeswax
70g (2¼ oz) cocoa butter
1 tsp coconut oil
5 drops lemon balm tincture
5 drops calendula tincture
10 drops mandarin essential oil

Makes 80g (2¾oz)

Mandarin essential oil, expressed from the fresh peel of the fruit, is gently antiseptic and cleansing. Lemon balm is active against the herpes virus, so this balm will also help to prevent or treat cold sores. Cocoa butter helps to condition, soothe, and protect lips.

1 *Melt the beeswax*, cocoa butter, and coconut oil over a saucepan of hot water (bain-marie).

2 *Add the tinctures* and essential oil to the mixture, then stir.

3 *Divide between* two small sterilized jars and allow to set. It will keep for about 3 months.

Minty fresh foot cream

 MOISTURIZES SKIN   **ENERGIZES**

Makes 100g (3½oz)

Tired, aching feet will benefit from this cooling, refreshing foot cream, which includes both peppermint and spearmint (also known as garden mint) for maximum effect. Its soothing effects will alleviate any discomfort after a long day on the move, and also help to keep skin smooth and in good condition. It will keep for at least 2 months.

INGREDIENTS

2 tsp cocoa butter
2 tsp beeswax
2 tbsp almond oil
1 tbsp wheatgerm oil
2 tbsp spearmint infusion (p.29)
2 tsp emulsifying wax
10 drops peppermint essential oil

METHOD

1 Heat the cocoa butter, beeswax, and almond and wheatgerm oils together in a bowl set over a saucepan of boiling water (bain-marie) until the ingredients have melted.
2 Warm the spearmint infusion gently in a saucepan, but do not allow to boil. Dissolve the emulsifying wax in it. Take the oily mixture off the heat, slowly add the infusion, and stir until cool.
3 Add the peppermint essential oil, decant into a sterilized glass jar (such as a screw-cap or kilner jar) with a tight-fitting lid and store in the refrigerator.

"This cooling, soothing cream, which includes both peppermint and spearmint for maximum effect, will bring relief to hot, aching feet after a long day"

Stimulating body oil

 MOISTURIZES SKIN   **ENERGIZES**

Makes approx 100ml (3½fl oz)

The wonderfully enriching base of plant oils in this body oil is rich in natural essential fatty acids, minerals, and vitamins to restore suppleness and elasticity to the skin. A stimulating aromatherapy blend of peppermint, juniper, lavender, and rosemary also boosts the circulation and invigorates the senses.

INGREDIENTS

4 tsp almond oil
4 tsp sunflower oil
4 tsp coconut oil
4 tsp grapeseed oil
2 tsp avocado oil
2 tsp wheatgerm oil
10 drops lavender essential oil
10 drops peppermint essential oil
10 drops juniper essential oil
10 drops rosemary essential oil

METHOD

1 Blend all the ingredients together.
2 Store in a sterilized dark glass bottle with a tight-fitting lid and use within 3 months.

Geranium and orange body oil

 MOISTURIZES SKIN   **REVITALIZES**

Makes approx 100ml (3½fl oz)

This enriching body oil treats both body and mind to bring a deep sense of well-being. It is an excellent all-purpose skin-conditioning or massage oil, with a bright, sunny scent. Geranium essential oil has a balancing effect on the skin and is used by aromatherapists to help treat anxiety and tension, while orange essential oil is toning and refreshing.

INGREDIENTS

2½ tbsp almond oil
2½ tbsp sunflower oil
4 tsp calendula macerated oil
20 drops geranium essential oil
20 drops orange essential oil

METHOD

1 Blend all the ingredients together.
2 Store in a sterilized dark glass bottle with a tight-fitting lid and use within 3 months.

Detox body oil

 **MOISTURIZES SKIN**   **STIMULATES CIRCULATION**

Makes approx 100ml (3½fl oz)

A stimulating and detoxifying blend of oils like this can help to boost the circulation and strengthen and tone the skin for a smoother appearance. For the best results, try dry-skin brushing your body with a natural bristle brush before having a warm bath or shower, then massage the body oil into your skin.

INGREDIENTS

2½ tbsp soya oil
2½ tbsp almond oil
4 tsp wheatgerm oil
5 drops lemon essential oil
5 drops frankincense essential oil
5 drops orange essential oil
2 drops juniper essential oil
2 drops black pepper essential oil
2 drops vetiver essential oil
2 drops eucalyptus essential oil

METHOD

1 Blend all the ingredients together.
2 Store in a sterilized dark glass bottle with a tight-fitting lid and use within 3 months.

Calendula and St John's wort soothing oil

 **SOOTHES SUNBURN AND SHINGLES**

Makes enough for 1 treatment

Always try to protect your skin from overexposure to the sun, but if you do accidentally get sunburnt, use this soothing oil to ease the discomfort. Do not apply before any exposure to the sun, as St John's wort is known to be photosensitizing. This oil blend can also be applied to relieve the pain of shingles.

INGREDIENTS

1 tsp calendula oil
1 tsp St John's wort oil
2 drops lavender essential oil

METHOD

Blend the ingredients together and gently apply to the skin.

Lemon (*Citrus limon*)
As well as cleansing and toning the skin, lemon essential oil also encourages mental focus.

Bergamot and mint deodorant

 DEODORIZES

Makes approx 85ml (2¾fl oz)

A refreshing combination of witch hazel and lavender water are the main ingredients for this fragrant underarm body spray, which keeps skin fresh. It also contains a cleansing, antibacterial blend of essential oils that includes citrussy bergamot, grapefruit, and lemon and invigorating peppermint and woody cypress. Spray on clean, dry skin. May also be used on the feet.

INGREDIENTS

1 tsp vegetable glycerin
2½ tbsp witch hazel
2½ tbsp lavender water
10 drops bergamot essential oil
8 drops grapefruit essential oil
7 drops lemon essential oil
4 drops peppermint essential oil
1 drop cypress essential oil

METHOD

1 Combine the vegetable glycerin with the witch hazel.
2 Stir in the essential oils.
3 Store in a sterilized dark glass bottle with a fine mist atomizer. Shake well before use to ensure the ingredients are well blended. Use within 6 months.

Rose body splash

 STIMULATES THE SENSES

Makes approx 95ml (3¼fl oz)

This subtle, floral body splash features a luxurious blend of damask rose flower water and earthy patchouli and bright geranium essential oils. Aloe vera and rose water are both gentle, soothing, and cooling – a perfect combination to pep up tired skin. For extra refreshment in hot weather, store the bottle in the refrigerator in between each use.

INGREDIENTS

75ml (2½fl oz) distilled water
2 tsp aloe vera juice
2 tsp rose flower water
3 drops rose absolute essential oil
3 drops geranium essential oil
1 drop patchouli essential oil

METHOD

1 Combine all the ingredients.
2 Store in a sterilized dark glass bottle with a fine mist atomizer. Shake before use to ensure the ingredients are well blended. Use within 2 months.

Geranium and orange body splash

 REVITALIZES

Makes approx 95ml (3¼fl oz)

With its bright, sunny fragrance, this body spray refreshes the skin, lifts the spirits, and leaves the skin lightly scented. Aloe vera, which makes a cooling, soothing base, is combined with earthy vetiver and brightly scented geranium oils and delicately scented orange flower water, made from the blossom of the bitter orange tree.

INGREDIENTS
80ml (2¾fl oz) distilled water
2 tsp aloe vera juice
1 tsp orange flower water
2 drops patchouli essential oil
1 drop geranium essential oil

METHOD
1 Combine all the ingredients.
2 Store in a sterilized dark glass bottle with a fine mist atomizer. Shake well before use to ensure the ingredients are well blended. Use within 2 months.

Frankincense body splash

 ENERGIZES

Makes approx 95ml (3¼fl oz)

Frankincense essential oil, which is distilled from the resin of the tree, is gently astringent and has a toning effect on the skin. Combined with fresh citrus oils of mandarin and bergamot orange, it creates a subtly scented blend that has cleansing and revitalising properties and will refresh all skin types.

INGREDIENTS
5½ tbsp distilled water
2 tsp aloe vera juice
1 tsp lavender flower water
4 drops frankincense essential oil
2 drops mandarin essential oil
2 drops bergamot essential oil

METHOD
1 Combine all the ingredients.
2 Store in a sterilized dark glass bottle with a fine mist atomizer. Shake before use. Use within 2 months.

Geranium (Pelargonium graveolens)
Geranium is used in aromatherapy to treat the skin, and as a remedy to alleviate tiredness and fatigue.

MAKING TONERS

Toners are used after cleansing to help refine the skin and maintain its pH balance; they also remove any last traces of cleanser before moisturizing. If you have very sensitive skin, test any skin product on a small area of skin first to check that it does not provoke a reaction.

Lavender and aloe vera toner

 TONES SKIN

Makes 100ml (3½fl oz)

This refreshing toner is suitable for all skin types, especially problem skin, and contains a stimulating aromatherapy blend to cleanse the skin and regulate oiliness: witch hazel and lavender waters create a gently astringent and purifying base to tone the pores of the skin and promote a clear complexion. Use within 6 months.

INGREDIENTS

80ml (2¾fl oz) lavender
   flower water
2 tsp witch hazel
1 tsp aloe vera juice
14 drops bergamot essential oil
4 drops lemon essential oil
4 drops petitgrain essential oil
4 drops lavender essential oil
2 drops rosemary essential oil
2 drops black pepper essential oil

METHOD

1 Combine all the ingredients thoroughly.
2 Store in a sterilized glass bottle, preferably with an atomizer spray, out of direct sunlight, and shake well before use.

Lemon (Citrus limon) *The ripe peel of fresh lemons contains an essential oil that is refreshing, cleansing, and tonifying.*

Rose toner

 TONES SKIN

Makes 100ml (3½fl oz)

This simple toner refreshes and balances the skin. Rose soothes while vinegar, which has a tonic action, stimulates circulation and helps to regulate the skin's natural pH. Apple cider vinegar – produced by a simple fermentation process that retains all the apples' nutritional goodness – is fortified with extra enzymes produced during fermentation.

INGREDIENTS

85ml (2¾fl oz) mineral water
2 heaped tsp dried, or 4 heaped tsp fresh rose petals
1 tsp dried, or 2 tsp fresh elderflower
1 tbsp apple cider vinegar

METHOD

1 Make an infusion (p.29) with the water, rose petals, and elderflower. Once cooled, add the cider vinegar and pour into a sterilized glass bottle with a tight-fitting lid.
2 Shake well before each use to blend. Apply after cleansing on cotton wool or with a muslin cloth. Gently wipe over the skin. Refrigerate and use within 3 months.

Herbal toner

 TONES SKIN

Makes 100ml (3½fl oz)

Witch hazel extract is a useful remedy that helps to calm and refresh tired skin. Its astringent properties also help regulate the production of sebum and minimize pores for a more even skin tone. Combined with anti-inflammatory chamomile, balancing rose, and stimulating rosemary, this gentle toner is suitable for all skin types

INGREDIENTS

75 ml (2½fl oz) distilled water
1 tbsp witch hazel
2 tsp aloe vera
3 drops chamomile blue essential oil
3 drops rosemary essential oil
3 drops rose absolute essential oil

METHOD

1 Combine all the ingredients and decant into a sterilized glass bottle with a tight-fitting lid.
2 Shake well before each use to blend. Apply after cleansing on cotton wool or with a muslin cloth. Gently wipe over the skin. Refrigerate and use within 3 months.

Herbal face and body spritz

 REVITALIZES SKIN

Makes 100ml (3½fl oz)

Revitalizing fresh mint is the essential ingredient of this refreshing fragrant herbal spritz, which is ideal for hot summer days and nights to help cool your skin. Spray it in a fine mist over exposed skin on the face and body as often as required. Store in the refrigerator when not in use so the spritz stays fresh and cool, and use within 2 days.

INGREDIENTS
3 heaped tsp fresh mint
1 heaped tsp fresh dill
1 heaped tsp fresh parsley
85ml (2¾fl oz) mineral water

METHOD
Make an infusion (p.29) with the herbs (using just enough boiling water to cover the herbs). Once brewed, add the mineral water and pour into a sterilized glass bottle with an atomizer spray.

Refreshing facial spritz

 REVITALIZES SKIN　　 **ENERGIZES**

Makes 100ml (3½fl oz)

Orange flower water is a wonderfully restorative remedy for the skin, and aromatherapists use its delicate scent to help treat stress. This refreshing spritz is ideal to use when travelling to refresh the skin and ease the mind. Store in the refrigerator when not in use so the spritz stays fresh and cool, and use within 2 days.

INGREDIENTS
85ml (2¾fl oz) distilled water
2 tsp aloe vera juice
1 tsp orange flower water
1 drop propolis tincture
1 drop lemon essential oil
1 drop rosemary essential oil

METHOD
Combine all the ingredients and decant into a sterilized glass bottle with an atomizer spray. Shake well before each use.

Dill (Anethum graveolens)
A popular culinary herb due to its fragrant, lacy, frond-like leaves, dill is best used fresh.

MAKING BATH BOMBS

Fizzing bath bombs, which are easy to make and require only simple ingredients, are a delight to the senses. They make great presents, too – once you have pressed the mixture into a ball and wrapped it in kitchen foil, simply cover it in colourful tissue paper and decorate it with ribbons.

Citrus bath bombs

 SOOTHES TIRED MUSCLES   **REVITALIZES**

Makes 4 small bombs

This citrus bath bomb will always liven up bath time. Grapefruit, lemon, and lime essential oils are combined with fresh-scented rosemary essential oil to release a vibrant fragrance as the ingredients fizz and dissolve in the water. You can add some colour by replacing the almond oil with green avocado oil or orange carrot oil.

INGREDIENTS

80g (2¾ oz) sodium bicarbonate
1 tbsp citric acid
4 drops grapefruit essential oil
4 drops lemon essential oil
1 drop lime essential oil
1 drop rosemary essential oil
a pinch of dried calendula
   petals, chopped
a dash of carrot oil (optional)
a dash of avocado oil (optional)
finely chopped herbs or
   flowers (optional)

METHOD

1 Mix the sodium bicarbonate and citric acid together on a plate. Sprinkle the essential oils onto the sodium bicarbonate mixture and add the calendula petals.

2 If you want to add some colour to your bath bomb, add a dash of carrot oil to give an orange colour, or avocado oil for a green tint. You might also like to add finely chopped herbs such as mint, or flowers including lavender or calendula.

3 Use the mixture as a powder sprinkled directly into the bath, or press firmly into shaped moulds such as old camera film cases, ice-cube trays, and pastry cutters. Add the powder or block to the bath water just before you step into the bath.

4 To make the bath bomb into a present, simply press the mixture into a round ball, wrap it in aluminium foil, cover the foil with tissue paper, and add some ribbons or other decorations.

Exotic bath bombs

 **SOOTHES TIRED MUSCLES**  **STIMULATES THE SENSES**

Makes 4 small bombs

Just add this sensually scented fizzing bath bomb to running bath water to make bathtime a special occasion. The powdery mix softens the water, while the aromatherapeutic blend of earthy vetiver, exotic Madagascan ylang ylang flowers, and warm, relaxing citrus brings peace of mind and a deep sense of well-being.

INGREDIENTS

3 tbsp sodium bicarbonate
1 tbsp citric acid
4 drops mandarin essential oil
3 drops vetiver essential oil
2 drops ylang ylang essential oil
1 petitgrain essential oil
2 tsp St John's wort (hypericum) macerated oil
a pinch of rose petals, finely chopped

METHOD

1 Mix the sodium bicarbonate and citric acid together on a flat plate. Add the essential oils by sprinkling them over the powder.
2 Use a spoon to heap the powder into the centre of the plate. Make a small well in the centre of the powder, add the deep red St John's wort oil and the rose petals.
3 Gradually mix the powder, oil, and rose petals together. The hypericum oil helps the ingredients to bind together, as well as add colour.
4 Press the mixture firmly into shaped moulds such as ice-cube trays or pastry cutters, or simply hand-mould the ingredients into balls. Store in a dry place and use within 2 months.

Ginger and juniper warming foot soak

 WARMS UP THE BODY   **STIMULATES CIRCULATION**

Makes enough for 1 treatment

This aromatic soak boosts the circulation and eliminates the chill from cold feet. Ginger has long been used for its warming action, while juniper is stimulating and cloves have mild pain-relieving properties. The aromatic bay leaves and orange peel in this therapeutic blend also delight the senses as the foot soak takes effect.

INGREDIENTS

1 tbsp dried rosehips
2 tbsp dried hibiscus
1 tsp cloves
1 tsp juniper berries
3 bay leaves, crushed
1 tbsp orange peel, fresh or dried
3 drops ginger essential oil

METHOD

1 Place all the ingredients in a muslin (cheesecloth) bag and gently stir the bag in a large bowl of boiling water.
2 After 10 minutes, add sufficient cold water to make the soak a comfortable temperature, but still hot. Immerse your feet in the liquid for as long as is comfortable, or until the water has cooled.

Sunshine bath bombs

 SOOTHES TIRED
MUSCLES　　 REVITALIZES

Makes 4 small bombs

This gentle yet warmly scented fizzing bath bomb is ideal for children, lifting the spirits but also calming the emotions with its warm, citrus scents of mandarin and orange combined with soothing, relaxing lavender. Golden calendula oil and grated citrus zest give the bomb added colour and texture.

INGREDIENTS
3 tbsp sodium bicarbonate
1 tbsp citric acid
7 drops mandarin essential oil
2 drops orange essential oil
1 drop lavender essential oil
2 tsp calendula oil
a pinch of orange, mandarin, or
　lemon peel, finely grated

METHOD
1 Mix the sodium bicarbonate and citric acid on a flat plate. Add the essential oils by sprinkling them over the powder, then use a spoon to heap the powder into the centre of the plate.
2 Make a small well in the centre, add the calendula oil, and gradually mix it into the powder to bind the bath bomb together. It will also add a little colour. Add the citrus peel zest whilst mixing.
3 Press the mixture firmly into shaped moulds such as ice-cube trays, pastry cutters or simply hand-mould the ingredients into balls. Store in a dry place, and use within 2 months.

Relax and restore bath herbs

 RELAXES　　 SOOTHES TIRED MUSCLES

Makes enough for 1 bath treatment

Mildly astringent, tannin-rich raspberry leaves blend well with skin-soothing violet and relaxing lavender to create this fragrant, skin-friendly wash that eases the mind and body. Oatmeal has also been included, as it is known to be an excellent remedy for dry skin: it gently softens and nurtures the skin to leave it feeling smooth and moisturized.

INGREDIENTS
2 tbsp raspberry leaves
2 tbsp violet leaf
2 tbsp lavender
2 tbsp oatmeal, powdered

METHOD
1 Combine the herbs and oatmeal and grind in a pestle and mortar (or a coffee grinder or blender) to make a rough powder.
2 Place the powder in a muslin bag. Hang the bag under the taps while running your bath so that the warm water flows through the herbs, then add the bag to your bath water. Lie back and relax.

Stimulating hair oil

 **TREATS ALL
HAIR TYPES**

Makes enough for 1 treatment

Rich, green avocado oil is pressed from the flesh of the fruit rather than the seed. It is vitamin- and mineral-rich, as well as being high in essential fatty acids, and is extremely moisturizing. Tonifying rosemary and basil essential oils are also added to stimulate hair growth in this intensive conditioning treatment.

INGREDIENTS

2 tsp avocado oil
2 drops rosemary essential oil
2 drops basil essential oil

METHOD

1 Mix the avocado oil and essential oils together and decant into a bottle. Heat the oils by placing the bottle in a bowl of hot water.

2 Massage the oil into the scalp with firm circular movements with the pads of your fingers. Leave the mixture on the hair for 30 minutes, then shampoo as usual. Applying your shampoo before wetting your hair makes it easier to remove the hair oil. Use within 6 months.

Sweet basil (Ocimum basilicum) *In aromatherapy, basil is used to help clear the mind and relieve intellectual fatigue, while giving clarity and mental strength.*

Thyme and cider rinse

 TREATS DANDRUFF

Makes 100ml (3½fl oz)

Thyme essential oil is warming and stimulating, has strong antifungal and antibacterial properties, and is traditionally used to give hair added strength. Apple cider vinegar makes a wonderfully cleansing, shine-enhancing hair tonic. This simple combination makes an excellent pre-wash treatment for anyone prone to dandruff.

INGREDIENTS

100ml (3½fl oz) apple cider vinegar
10 drops thyme essential oil

METHOD

Blend the ingredients together and massage into the scalp. Leave for up to 5 minutes. Rinse with warm water and shampoo as usual. Use within 6 months.

Calendula and banana hair treatment

 TREATS ALL
HAIR TYPES

Makes enough for 1 treatment

Bananas are rich in potassium and amino acids, and make a great treatment for smoothing and nourishing dry or damaged hair. Combined with antioxidant calendula macerated oil and exotic ylang ylang, this simple but effective moisturizing hair mask is particularly effective for taming unruly or frizzy curls.

INGREDIENTS
1 ripe banana
2 tsp calendula macerated oil
3 drops ylang ylang essential oil
A dash of lemon juice to add to rinse

METHOD
1 Use a blender to purée the banana to a smooth paste (this will make it easier to rinse from your hair), then combine with the calendula and ylang ylang oils.
2 Wet your hair, squeeze out the excess water with a towel to leave hair damp, comb through, then apply the banana paste by massaging it into the hair.
3 Cover your hair with clingfilm, an old showercap, or a large plastic food bag (this will stop the mixture drying out) and leave for 30 minutes. Wash out the mask using your normal shampoo with a dash of added lemon juice.

Horsetail shampoo for dull hair

 TREATS DULL HAIR

Makes 100ml (3½fl oz)

Silica-rich horsetail is a traditional remedy used to restore vitality to lack-lustre hair. Combined with classic, shine-boosting, growth-encouraging rosemary, cooling, oil-balancing sage, and rich almond oil, it moisturizes and nourishes hair to make it stronger and healthier. It also enhances natural shine and bounce.

INGREDIENTS
3 tbsp ordinary shampoo
3 tbsp infusion of equal parts
  horsetail, rosemary, and sage
scant 1 tsp almond oil
6 drops rosemary essential oil

METHOD
Blend all the ingredients together well. Use within 1 week, or keep refrigerated and use within 2 weeks.

Acknowledgments

Neal's Yard Remedies would like to thank the following for their valuable contribution to making this book happen: Julie Wood, Elly Phillips, Dr Pauline Hili and the NYR technical team past and present, and Dr Merlin Willcox.

Dorling Kindersley would like to thank the team at Neal's Yard Remedies, Peacemarsh, for the use of the organic physic garden in July and August 2010 for many of the herb photographs in this book. We would also like to thank Philip Robbshow at Sheepdrove Organic Farm for his help.

Thanks to the following for supplying plants for photography: Arne Herbs, Jekka's Herb Farm, Petersham Nurseries, Poyntzfield Herb Nursery, and South Devon Chilli Farm.

Illustrations Debbie Maizels
Art direction Luis Peral, Nicky Collings
Food styling Jane Lawrie
Prop styling Wei Tang
Proofreading Jennifer Latham
Recipe testing Katy Greenwood
Editorial assistance Roxanne Benson-Mackey, Kajal Mistry
Design assistance Danaya Bunnag, Emma Forge
DK Picture Library Lucy Claxton, Romaine Werblow

The Authors

Susan Curtis
Susan runs a busy practice as a homeopath and naturopath and is the Director of Natural Health for Neal's Yard Remedies. She is the author of several books, including Essential Oils, and co-author of Natural Healing for Women. Susan has two children and is passionate about helping people to live a more natural and healthy lifestyle.

Louise Green
An avid supporter of the organic movement and eco-living, Louise has spent 15 years at Neal's Yard Remedies in a variety of roles ranging from buying to product development, and most recently as Head of Sustainability. Louise lives in London and is expecting her first child.

Penelope Ody MNIMH
Penelope qualified as a medical herbalist in the 1980s and practised as a consultant herbalist for 12 years. Since then she has written more than 20 books on both Western and Chinese herbalism and runs workshops on traditional uses of culinary and medicinal herbs at her home in Hampshire.

Dragana Vilinac
A fourth-generation herbalist widely respected for her vast knowledge and expertise, Dragana's passion for herbal medicine has taken her around the world, and has led her to train in disciplines including Western Herbal Medicine and Traditional Chinese Medicine. Dragana is Head Herbalist for Neal's Yard Remedies.